THREE STRATEGIES
OF
HUANG SHI GONG

黄石公三略

ASIAPAC COMIC SERIES
STRATEGY & LEADERSHIP

The Art of Government

THREE STRATEGIES OF HUANG SHI GONG

黃石公三略

WANG XUANMING

Translated by
Alan Chong

ASIAPAC • SINGAPORE

Publisher
ASIAPAC BOOKS PTE LTD
629 Aljunied Road #04-06
Cititech Industrial Building
Singapore 1438
Tel: 7453868
Fax: 7453822

First published November 1993
Reprinted March 1994

© ASIAPAC BOOKS, 1993
ISBN 981-3029-14-5

Cover design by Bay Song Lin
Typeset by Quaser Technology Pte Ltd
Body text in 8/9 pt Helvetica
Printed in Singapore by
Loi Printing Pte Ltd

Publisher's Note

Three Strategies of Huang Shi Gong is one of the military classics in *Wu Jing Qi Shu (The Seven Books of War)* that was used as a standard reference for military officials in China. To have it now in comic form allows both the young and the adult readers, especially those interested in Chinese culture, access to a great military classic in a fun and entertaining way.

We are pleased to present the work of Wang Xuanming, a contemporary cartoonist from Mainland China. His earlier books in this series, *Thirty-six Stratagems, Six Strategies for War* and *Gems of Chinese Wisdom* have been warmly received by our readers. *Three Strategies of Huang Shi Gong* is the fourth book.

We feel honoured to have cartoonist Wang Xuanming's permission to the translation rights to his best-selling comics. We would also like to thank Mr Alan Chong for translating this volume and writing the Foreword, Mr Chiang Ming Yu for his review, and the production team for putting in their best effort in the publication of this series.

Strategy and Leadership Series:

The Art of War : Chinese Military Classic
Thirty-six Stratagems : Secret Art of War
Six Strategies for War : The Practice of Effective Leadership
Gems of Chinese Wisdom : Mastering the Art of Leadership
Three Strategies of Huang Shi Gong : The Art of Government
100 Strategies of War : Brilliant Tactics in Action

Three Strategies of Huang Shi Gong is the latest addition to a series of ancient Chinese military classics in comic form. Illustrated with examples from China's war-filled history, many of the lessons are actually directly applicable to human resource management.

The second of the three strategies in this book, the Middle Strategy, is aptly subtitled "The secret of controlling generals and officials". The Upper Strategy abound with lessons that leaders would best apply to themselves. For example, in the section about the eight moral qualities of a commander, Di Gong went through thick and thin with his men in defence of Liuzhong city. Consequently, his men respected him and stuck with him as a cohesive unit even though there were only thirteen of them left when reinforcements lifted the siege one year later.

In the Lower Strategy, subtitled "The strategy of governing with the ways of the sage and the worthy", I was struck by the fact that the first lesson was titled "Able men are the foundation of a state". This is even more true for a small nation like ours! As Bertolt Brecht once wrote, "The finest plans have always been spoiled by the littleness of them that should carry them out. Even emperors can't do it all by themselves."

The story of the origin of the book on which this adaptation is based makes Huang Shi Gong, the book's original author, seem almost supernatural. But intellect is after all a gift from God, the difference being in how we use it.

I hope this book helps readers to better exercise their intellect, and may you gain as much enjoyment from it as I have.

Chiang Ming Yu
Chairman, Wargame Club
Singapore Armed Forces Reservists' Association

About the Editor/Illustrator

Wang Xuanming, a contemporary cartoonist in China, was born in Beijing in 1950. He was trained formally in commercial art and industrial art. Since 1972, he has been engaged in various aspects of artistic work, even undertaking the production of screen advertisements and artistic stage designs. Wang's contribution to the field of art is immense. He frequently explores various ways of expressing his artistic talents. Besides a lot of cartoons, picture books, and illustrations, he also does oil paintings and posters. His works have on many occasions entered nationwide art exhibitions, won awards in several art competitions, and have been selected for inclusion in various art albums.

Wang's cartoons, illustrations, and other works have been serialized in all the major newspapers and publications in Beijing since 1980. His cartoons entitled *Different Gravitational Force* is praised by famous Chinese artists, and was selected for inclusion in the *Anthology of Chinese Scientific Cartoons*. In 1987, he participated in the creation of the animated cartoon *Brother Elephant*, which captured the hearts of many children when it was first shown on television.

Wang has worked with many publishers in Beijing, such as China Friendly Publishing Co., Chinese Cultural Publishing Co., Huaxia Publishing Co., People's Art Publishing Co., and Zhaohua Publishing Co. He has gained the trust and confidence of both publishers and artists alike.

In his latest comic series, *Books of Strategy*, he uses a simple and humorous art form to introduce ancient Chinese military classics to modern readers. The books were very well received by people from all walks of life when they were first published in China; the Beijing Radio Station made a special interview of this series of books and highly recommended it to the public. This series is published by China Friendly Publishing Co. in China, and by Treasure Creation Co. Ltd. in Hongkong. Asiapac Books in Singapore is the publisher for the English edition of this series.

Wang is at present an art editor at the *China Science and Technology Daily*.

Preface

Shi Ji (*Book of History* or *Records of the Historian*), the respected work of a renowned Western Han Dynasty historiographer, Sima Qian, is celebrated for its rigorous selection of materials and faithfulness to history. But its entry about Huang Shi Gong surprisingly seems more like a fairy tale.

According to *Shi Ji*, Zhang Liang, a prince of the vanquished state of Han during the Warring States Era, was hotheaded and simple-minded in his youth. A fanatic bent on restoring his vanquished state, he hired a man to assassinate Qin Shi Huang. His rash action not only resulted in the death of the assassin, but also made him a wanted man.

But ten years later, the brash young man had transformed himself into a completely different person. He became a senior strategist of Liu Bang and was instrumental in the founding of the Han Dynasty after destroying the Qin Dynasty. In the arduous uprising against Qin and the subsequent power struggle against Xiang Yu, Zhang Liang demonstrated his prowess as a brilliant strategist on many occasions. First, he helped Liu Bang to win the race in capturing the Qin capital of Xianyang by taking the key cities of Wancheng and Yaoguan and pressing on to Bashang.

Despite being the underdog in the ensuing power struggles between Chu and Han, Liu Bang was able to turn the tables on his militarily superior rival by a series of brilliant moves engineered by Zhang Liang. These included the burning of a plank way to lure the Chu army into complacency; visiting his troops to boost their morale even when he was seriously injured; the temporary installation of Han Xing as king to win anti-Chu support and conferring a title on his past foe, Yong Chi, to consolidate his nascent regime. It is with little wonder that Liu Bang praised Zhang Liang as a great minister capable of "sitting within a command tent and devising strategies that will assure victory a thousand *li* away".

According to Sima Qian, the main reason for the dramatic transformation of Zhang Liang from a reckless youth to a resourceful strategist within a short time of ten years was that he had mastered the essence of *Three Strategies of Huang Shi Gong*, the wonderful military book given by the mysterious recluse he chanced upon.

Three Srategies of Huang Shi Gong is reputedly mankind's oldest monograph on tactical warfare. It is divided into three parts: the Upper Strategy, the Middle Strategy and the Lower Strategy. The Upper Strategy advocates the philosophy of using the soft to overcome the strong. The Middle Strategy discusses the strategy tor controlling generals and the masses. The Lower Strategy stresses the importance of governing a country by the ways of sages.

Because the book was too explicit on the secrets of state administration and the ways of controlling generals and the people, together with other major military classics, it was banned by the emperors of the Tang and the Song Dynasty for fear that its public circulation would nurture potential rebels.

Officially, however, *Three Strategies of Huang Shi Gong* was a military reference held in high esteem by the ruling class of successive dynasties. By the Northern Song Dynasty, it was elevated to be one of the *Wu Jing Qi Shu,* or *The Seven Books of War.*

With the view of promoting Chinese culture and giving readers a glimpse of the wisdom of the ancient Chinese, I have used cartoon as a means of interpreting this military classic. I hope you will enjoy it and perhaps find a useful pointer or two from some of the historical lessons and thoughts of ancient wise men.

Wang Xuanming

Translator's Note

There are two notable sages in Chinese history: Confucius, the civil sage, and Jiang Shang, better known as Jiang Tai Gong, the military sage.

Jiang Shang was a brilliant general, strategist and political thinker credited with helping King Wen and King Wu establish the Zhou Dynasty about eleventh century BC. He was so famous a military figure that three Chinese military classics have been popularly attributed to him. One of these is *Three Strategies of Huang Shi Gong.*

As with many ancient Chinese works, scholars differ in opinion as to who its author actually was. Nevertheless, the strongest research evidence attributes it to a recluse who wrote it in the final years of the Western Han Dynasty (206 BC - AD 24).

There is a well-known story in Sima Qian's *Shi Ji (Book of History* or *Records of the Historian)* on how the book surfaced and how the name Huang Shi Gong, or Yellowstone Elder, came about. This story is retold in detail in the opening chapter of the current book.

Since its appearance some 2,000 years ago, *Three Strategies of Huang Shi Gong* has been greatly valued by rulers of successive dynasties. During the Northern Song Dynasty, the book was officially designated one of the seven major military classics collectively called *Wu Jing Qi Shu (The Seven Books of War).* Due to its importance, scholars through the ages have come up with numerous annotations of the book. This has resulted in more than 140 surviving versions of the book.

During the reign of Emperor Uda (AD 887-897), *Three Strategies of Huang Shi Gong* was introduced to Japan where it was translated into Japanese and extensively studied by Japanese scholars and rulers. In 1777, it was introduced to North Korea and subsequently to other countries. A book of some 5,500 characters, *Three Strategies of Huang Shi Gong* is reputedly man's oldest monograph on political and military strategies.

Huang Shi Gong, the mysterious old man, said when he handed the original text of this book to Zhang Liang: "Study this book seriously and you could become the teacher of the emperor." After studying the book for more than ten years and mastering its contents, Zhang Liang was transformed from a reckless young man to a wise strategist who went on to assist Liu Bang to establish the Han Dynasty.

Unlike Zhang Liang, you probably will not become advisers to state rulers after reading this interpretation of the legendary classic by renowned Chinese cartoonist Wang Xuanming. But the historical lessons and the wisdom of ancient Chinese thinkers it contains may well give you some useful pointers as you tackle the complex issues of modern life.

Alan Chong

About the Translator

Alan Chong is a professional translator who undertakes a wide range of Chinese-English and English-Chinese translation assignments from literary works to technical and legal documents. He has also translated the following titles in Asiapac Comic Series: *Sayings of Han Fei Zi, A New Account of World Tales, Journey to the West Book I, Journey to the West Book II, Battle Domestica, Sour Pack,* and *Six Strategies for War.*

Contents

Huang Shi Gong

黃石公

Huang Shi Gong, or the Yellowstone Elder, was a mysterious ancient Chinese writer whose works have a profound influence on the history of China. In addition to this book, there are more than twenty other titles to his credit. They cover a wide range of subjects including military commandership, art of war, astrology, divination and stratagems.

Three Strategies of Huang Shi Gong, the most famous of the author's works, was designated by Emperor Shenzong of the Song Dynasty as one of *Wu Jing Qi Shu,* or *The Seven Books of War.*

1

He'll die!

The Qin emperor will be passing by Bolangsha tomorrow....

This story about Huang Shi Gong appeared in *Shi Ji*, or *Book of History*. During the final years of the Qin Dynasty, Zhang Liang, an aristocrat of Han, hired a man to assassinate the Qin emperor.

2

The assassination attempt failed.

Luckily, I'm not in that carriage!

3

Catch the culprit!

The Qin emperor was furious and determined to find out who plotted against him.

5

21

Study this book well and you can be an emperor's teacher. There'll be a rebellion against Qin ten years from now. You'll find a yellow stone at the foot of Mt Gucheng when you pass by Jibei thirteen years from now. That yellow stone will be my personification.

22

The old man floated away as soon as he finished talking.

23

Heeding the old man's words, Zhang Liang studied the military book thoroughly and became a brilliant strategist.

24

Later, Zhang Liang indeed became the teacher of Liu Bang, the founder emperor of the Han Dynasty.

25

With Zhang Liang's help, Liu Bang toppled the Qin Dynasty, defeated his arch rival Xiang Yu, and unified China.

Passing by Jibei thirteen years after he parted with the old man, Zhang Liang really found a yellow stone at the foot of Mt Gucheng.

We really meet again, Teacher.

26

27

Zhang Liang took the yellow stone home and worshipped it. After his death, he was buried together with the stone.

28

Later, people called the old man Huang Shi Gong. This is what the *Book of History* records about the origin of Huang Shi Gong.

The Upper Strategy

上略

The philosophy of overcoming
the strong with the soft

Flexible employment of the principle of overcoming the strong with the soft

1

Lao Zi said:

The softest and weakest of all things is water.

2

But water can overcome a rock, so the soft can overcome the strong, too.

3

Being moderately "soft" is a virtue. Being "strong" but untempered with benevolence can cause unpopularity.

Strong.

Soft.

7 During the Spring and Autumn Era, Nan Kuai of Lu occupied Feidi and switched allegiance to Qi.

This will be Qi territory!

8 In spring the following year, a Lu army under General Su Gong attacked Feidi.

9 The Lu army suffered heavy casualties after many failed attempts to take the city.

The Lu army commander was furious.

Round up all Feidi people outside the city and put them in jail!

10

We can't do this!

Ye Qufu advised against it.

11

12

It's cold. This fur coat is for you.

We should be kind to the Feidi people outside the city.

13

Am I dreaming?

Help yourself with these meat dumplings.

14

> Is it so simple?

> If we show them we're caring masters, Nan Kuai will fall automatically.

15 If the Feidi people treat this place as home, they'll turn against Nan Kuai and leave the besieged city.

16 If we frighten the people with high-handedness, they'll turn against us.

> He's a veritable devil!

A sound strategy must be formulated according to changes in enemy situation.

1 People cannot see the truth of all things until it reveals itself.

2 The secrets of the universe must be learnt and mastered from progressive changes of things.

3 There aren't any fixed rules to follow in strategic warfare. It depends on how the enemy moves.

4

It is foolish to set your moves before knowing the enemy situation.

My battle plan is ...

?

The enemy troops have already returned home. He's still dreaming!

Thank you for your advice, Teacher!

He who helps a ruler succeed by reading the enemy situation and acting according to circumstances can be the ruler's teacher.

5

During the Spring and Autumn Era, King Wu of Chu preceded his attack on Sui by sending a peace negotiator to Sui.

6

I'll decide on the way to attack according to the outcome of the peace negotiation.

7

Sui sent Shao Shi as its peace negotiator.

Shao Shi reported what he saw when he returned to Sui.

I saw only old, sickly soldiers in sloppy battle array. Their discipline was lax.

12

Such an army is easy meat. I suggest we attack them!

13

Shao Shi's right. Let's attack at once.

14

Don't fall into their trap, Your Majesty.

Ji Liang opposed.

15

16

Given the strength of Chu and the shrewdness of its king, it's improbable that they're attacking with a weak army. They must be feigning weakness.

17

The marquis of Sui heeded the advice, beefed up his defences and refrained from attacking. The king of Chu retreated, knowing that his ploy had failed.

18

Two years later, Chu invaded Sui again.

19

The Chu army seems to be well prepared and in high morale. We should feign a surrender first.

Ji Liang said to the marquis of Sui:

The wise should not reveal their true strength.

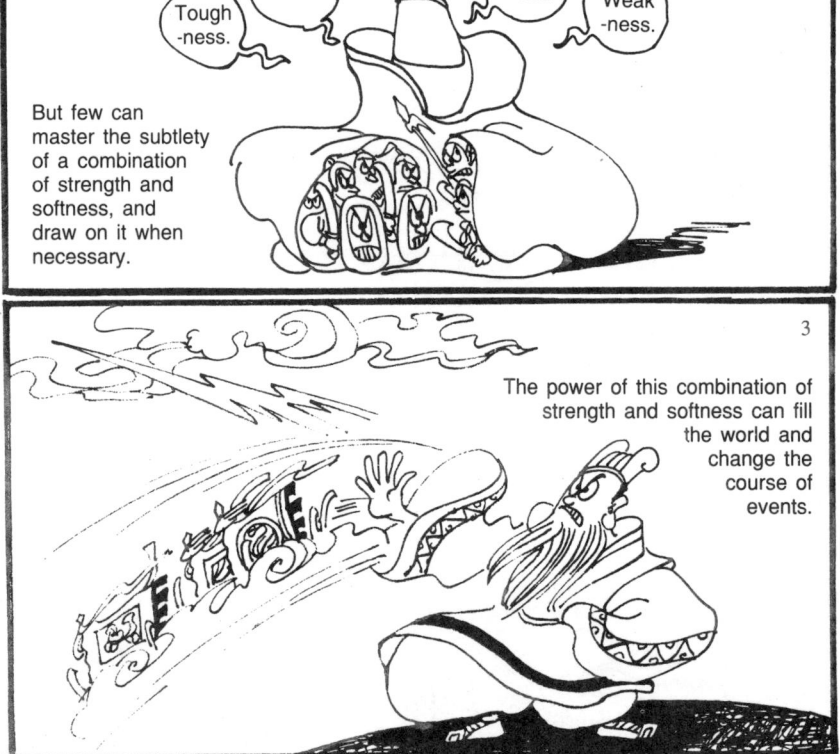

It's easy to seek to do others down and flaunt one's strength.

Tough-ness.

Strength.

Soft-ness.

Weak-ness.

But few can master the subtlety of a combination of strength and softness, and draw on it when necessary.

The power of this combination of strength and softness can fill the world and change the course of events.

4

Keeping it within and applying it flexibly can make your enemies submit to you.

5

Now, you're the king and you have everything. Won't you give Zhidi as a fief to your poor brother?

When Duke Zhuang of Zheng came to power in 743 BC, his mother, Jiang Shi, favoured his younger brother, Gongsu Duan.

6

Zhidi is strategically important. I'll agree to any other place you ask for.

7

Let him have Jingcheng then!

* 1 zhang = 3.3 metres

12 — A disaster is like weeds. Once allowed to spread, they'd be hard to eliminate. Even uncontrolled weeds can't be eliminated, let alone your pampered brother.

13 — An evildoer will trip and fall. Wait and see!

14 — With the backing from mom, who'd dare to touch us?

Gongsu Duan moved into Jingcheng and called himself Tai Shu*.

15 — Another ruler?

All of you shall obey my orders from now on. When I say go east, you don't go west!

Soon after, Tai Shu was issuing orders to officials at the western and northern borders.

26

* Grand Uncle

20 Without justice, he cannot unite the people. Too much power will bring him ruin instead.

Now's the time to act. He'll win the people's favour as he gains greater power.

General Gong Zilu again advised Duke Zhuang:

21 I want to have a taste of being the king, too.

Tai Shu intensified his preparation for war, stocking up food supplies and beefing up his forces.

22 When you attack, I'll help you from inside by opening the city gate.

You really love me, mum.

Tai Shu was ready for an attack on the state capital.

28

Duke Zhuang got wind of Tai Shu's impending attack.

Now's the time for action.

Tai Shu's about to attack.

23

He ordered General Gong Zilu:

Attack Jingcheng with 200 chariots!

24

Faster! Go faster!

Without the support of people in the city, Tai Shu's forces were easily defeated. Tai Shu escaped to Yandi and then to Gongguo.

25

26

A wise man conceals the wisdom of combining strength with suppleness and never acts rashly. This is what is meant by "supple without and tough within" and "weak without and strong within".

Understand others' psychology and use appropriate measures.

The key to success in military and state administration is to gain an insight into the people's psychology and apply appropriate measures.

ABC Psychology

You need a tranquillizer jab.

He who is in a dangerous situation, calm him. He who is afraid, make him brave.

He who deserts, recall and accommodate him. He who has been wronged, clear his name. He who appeals, give him a just hearing.

I'm not dreaming, am I?

Investigations show that you're innocent.

How dare you oppose the state. Jail him 100 years!

He who is humble, respect him. He who seeks to outdo others, control and restrain him. He who conspires, deal with him firmly.

He who loves wealth, make him rich. He who strives to achieve, give him a chance to win honour.

This is all yours if you succeed in your mission.

I'll go on a world tour first.

How embarrassing!

Only you and I will know.

He who errs and fears losing his reputation, promise him to keep it a secret.

This rascal's trying to hoodwink me again.

He who is astute and resourceful, make him a trusted aide. He who is fond of slandering others, scrutinize and warn him.

8 Any attempt at revolt, nib it in the bud. He who is arrogant, remind him to be humble.

You look a little stuck-up these few days.

9 He who surrenders, treat him properly.

I'll treat you like one of us.

10 During the Spring and Autumn Era, King Zhuang of Chu was holding a banquet for his officials and generals when a gust of wind blew out all the lights.

11 In the darkness, someone grabbed the king's favourite concubine. Struggling to break free, she pulled and broke the crest ribbon of the assailant.

12 Sobbing, she complained to the king:

Someone molested me and I broke his crest ribbon. Light the lights and we'll know who did it.

13

When you encourage the guest to drink, a little indiscretion is inevitable. How can we put him to shame for such a triviality?

The king consoled her and said:

14

Let's drink to our heart's content. Anyone without a broken crest ribbon hasn't drunk enough. He'll have to drink three more bowls!

So the king announced in darkness:

15

To please the king, all the guests broke their crest ribbons. The concubine could not identify her assailant when the lights were put on again.

16

In a war between Jin and Chu three years later, a Chu general fought so bravely that the Jin soldiers were terrified of him. The Jins were soundly defeated.

The art of enlisting able men.

Officials and generals of outstanding talents are the mainstay of a country. Diligent and law-abiding people are the foundation of a country.

Mainstay

Foundation

If a ruler can enlist heroes of the world, including talents from enemy states, then the enemy states will be impoverished and his country will grow stronger.

All my men are gone. I'm a veritable pauper!

A ruler who gives ranks of nobility, wealth and respect to able men will win their allegiance and loyalty.

I have all sorts of able men now.

35

Jin and Chu are enemies. The Jins are constantly scheming against us. How can Your Majesty still have the mood to hunt?

?!

King Zhuang of Chu often went hunting. His ministers advised him:

4

Well, playing could be beneficial to the state if done properly.

5

I'm afraid it's just an excuse.

Please enlighten us further.

6

7

I go hunting to seek brave men. He who dares to hunt tigers and leopards with a wooden stick reveals his bravery.

He who dares to fight a rhinoceros reveals his strength.

He who takes only the share of the quarry he deserves reveals his morality.

That's enough.

Through hunting, I enlist these three types of talent as leaders of our troops.

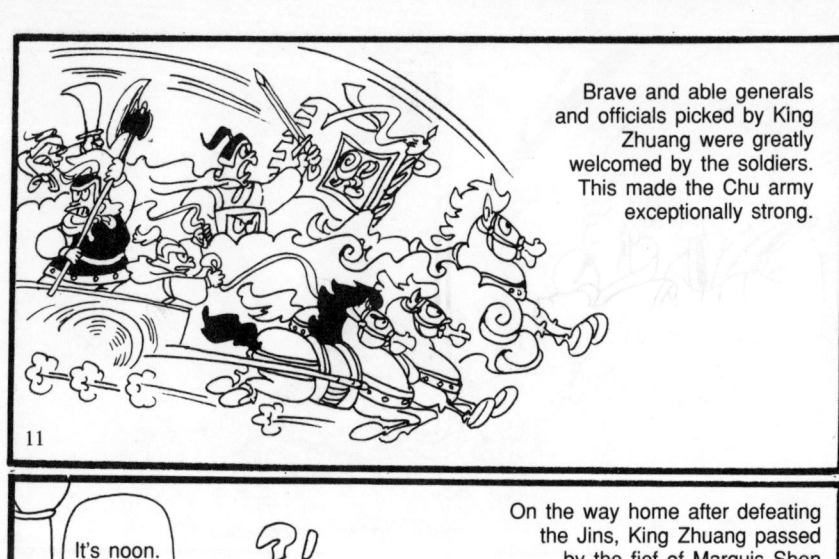

Brave and able generals and officials picked by King Zhuang were greatly welcomed by the soldiers. This made the Chu army exceptionally strong.

11

It's noon. Why isn't he eating?

On the way home after defeating the Jins, King Zhuang passed by the fief of Marquis Shen who entertained him to lunch.

12

It's noon and Your Majesty isn't eating. Please pardon me if I've done something wrong.

13

Thinking that he might have offended the king, the marquis said:

14

You've done nothing wrong.

15

I heard that a ruler who's able and has a good adviser can be a king.

16

A ruler who's of medium talent but has a good adviser can achieve hegemony.

17

A ruler who's mediocre and has officials inferior to him will lose his state.

Fools like you are only fit to be slaves.

18

I'm a low-calibre man and lack able men to assist me. I worry about losing the country!

There're many able people around but I'm unable to get them. So what's the use of eating?

19

20

News of King Zhuang thinking so much of enlisting able men as to forget his meal spread fast throughout the entire state.

Officials scrambled to offer their services and people began to recommend able men to the state. Until the death of King Zhuang, Chu's position as the hegemonic state had never been shaken.

21

It is most appropriate to make virtuous and able men the mainstay of a country. A wise ruler is constantly seeking and enlisting outstanding talents to be the foundation of the state and the military. Without the help of able men, a country can never be strong.

22

Kindness and favours at ordinary times ensure unity in times of war.

4

I invite all of you to share the mellow wine by drinking from the river!

Though a jar of wine could not flavour the water of a whole river, it did show the wish of the commander to share weal and woe with the soldiers.

5

Before the well in the camp yields water, the commander cannot say he is thirsty.

No, thanks!

Please have a drink!

6

Before the tent is set up, the commander cannot say he is tired.

Come on, faster!

7

43

When reinforcements arrived one year later, Di Gong was still holding out steadfastly though he was down to his last 13 men.

I'm proud of all of you!

16

An army whose commander treats his men with courtesy and respect and shares comforts and hardships with them at ordinary times is able to remain cohesive and fight with high morale in times of war.

17

18

A military commander who wishes to win over the hearts of his soldiers, make them submit to his command, motivate them to fight gallantly and withstand hardships, must be kind and helpful at ordinary times to earn their respect.

A commander must be mindful of his own moral cultivation.

He ought to be calm before a battle.

Don't worry. I already have a plan.

Chief, there're 200,000 enemy troops!

But, I'm your uncle!

According to the rules, I've to cut three months' pay from your salary.

He ought to be fair and reasonable.

He ought to be strict with military discipline. Every order must be enforced.

March!

7 He ought to be open to subordinates' views.

Your proposal's excellent. I'll record a merit for you.

Hee! Hee! He even accepts a private's views.

8 He ought to be good at `judging between right and wrong.

9 You're wrong!

He ought to be able to accommodate people with different talents.

I'll treat everyone equally.

10

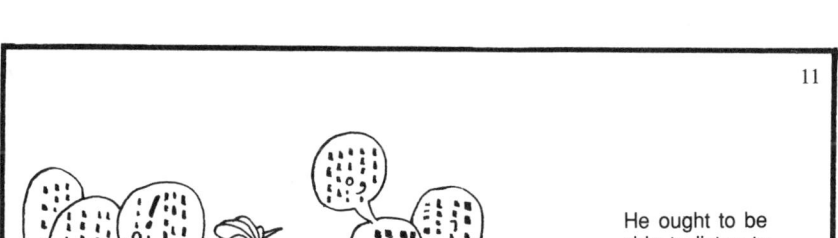

He ought to be able to listen to different views.

A commander who goes against these moral norms would be opposed by the masses and deserted by his followers, and suffer the misfortune of defeat and loss of his country.

Sun Zi's *Art of War* mentions wisdom, trustworthiness, benevolence, bravery and strictness as five moral criteria for a commander. The "Eight Virtues of a Commander" advocated in *Three Strategies of War* are even richer in content.

Encourage free airing of views and adopt sound strategies.

1 During the Three Kingdoms Era, Cao Cao launched an attack on Wuhuan against the advice of his officials.

Yuan Shang's only a fugitive. He won't be able to make use of the greedy Wuhuan people who don't think much of friendship.

2 It's not worth the long expedition to attack Wuhuan. Moreover, while you're away, Liu Bei'll certainly persuade Liu Biao to attack our capital...

3 Cao Cao ignored their advice and set off with his forces.

March!

4

There's no water within 200 *li**.

It was winter by the time Cao Cao crushed Wuhuan. Cold and dry weather made his homeward journey extremely difficult.

5

Cao Cao's men had to dig to a depth of more than 100 metres to get water.

Not a single grain of rice inside.

Mine, too.

There was also a shortage of food.

The Cao army had to kill several thousand battle horses for food.

How can I kill you after we've been through numerous battles together?

6

7

* 1 li = 0.5 km

8

Thank goodness, we've made it back alive!

After innumerable hardships, Cao Cao finally made it back to Xuchang, the capital.

9

Immediately upon his return, Cao Cao ordered:

Yes, sir!

Investigate thoroughly and give me a list of those who advised me against the expedition. Be sure not to leave out anyone!

10

I should've known better and shut up!

Not knowing what Cao Cao was up to, the people involved trembled in fear.

We've had it. We're doomed!

11

?!

This is a reward for the meritorious service you have rendered!

When the investigation was over, Cao Cao said to them:

12

I took a risk in the Wuhuan expedition and won by sheer good luck.

Cao Cao explained:

13

You gave sound advice. That's why I reward you. I hope in future you won't be afraid to speak up.

14

I should've said something too.

Cao Cao took the opportunity to encourage his men to air their views freely and come forward to offer their plans for helping him unite the world.

15

Qin Ershi, second emperor of the Qin Dynasty, did the opposite. He listened to Zhao Gao, the treacherous eunuch, and ended up losing all his good men and his life too.

With Zhao Gao around, you'll die regardless of whether you render meritorious service.

The more covert an attack, the higher the chances of success.

1

Please tell us something about the military action this time, chief.

A commander must keep his plans a secret.

No comment!

2

When the commander doesn't reveal anything, the enemy spies will be frustrated.

3

Once the commander's plans leak out, the army will lose all its advantages.

You'd better surrender! You've been surrounded. We knew your plans long ago.

We'll be in trouble if the four states conspire to attack us.

During the Warring States Era, the king of Qi called a meeting of the premiers of Yan, Zhao and Chu in Wei, but excluded the premier of Wei*.

I can foil the conspiracy of the four states if Your Majesty let me have 2,000 taels of gold.

Wei* general, Gongsun Yan said:

That'd be a small price to pay if you could sabotage their alliance plan.

The king of Wei* agreed.

According to this calculation, the king of Qi should be arriving in Wei soon.

Gongsun Yan calculated the date the king of Qi would arrive in Wei.

Wei = 衛   Wei* = 魏

That's simple. I'll let you see him first when he arrives.

The king of Wei agreed readily.

12

To understand the relationships between Yan, Zhao and Chu, we'll have to start from the very beginning...

Upon seeing the king of Qi, Gongsun Yan calmly began to talk about matters between the three states of Yan, Zhao and Chu.

13

This guy can really talk. My legs are aching.

Gongsun Yan kept on talking for half a day.

14

58

19

No matter how he explained, the premiers of the three states refused to believe him.

20

How could Gongsun Yan come all the way just for a chat?

Something must be going on.

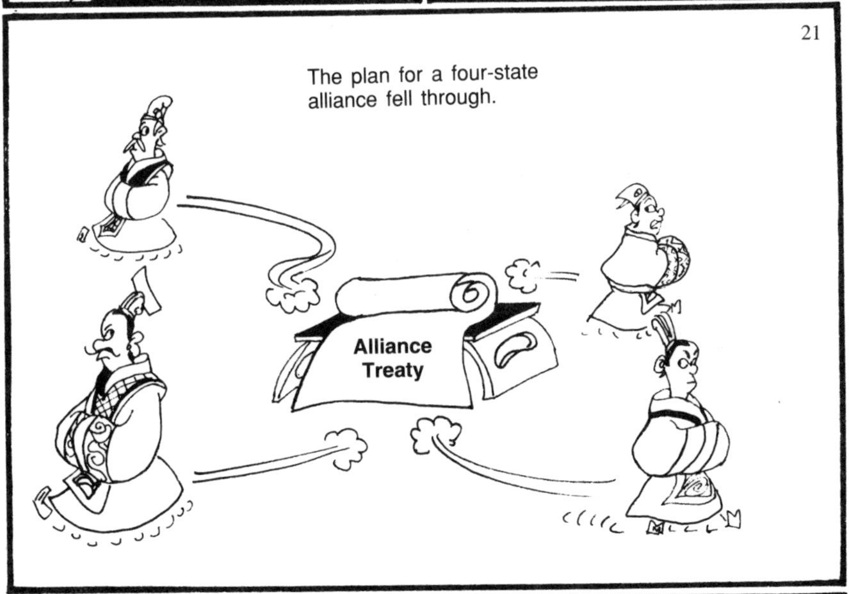

21

The plan for a four-state alliance fell through.

Alliance Treaty

22

Keeping the plans of the commander highly confidential will enable an army to surprise the enemy and ensure a swift victory.

Secret

**Plan well before a battle;
show anger
when anger is due.**

1. When a commander does not think deeply and plan ahead, his advisers will leave him.

帥

Can't talk on the same wavelength.

2. When a commander is not steady and brave, his subordinates will be fearful and uneasy.

Where's the chief?

He's gone!

3. When a commander acts rashly, the battle array of his army will not be steady.

One moment he shouts east, another moment he shouts west. It's a torture!

?!

12

That will fit the auspicious signs precisely!

13

The main purpose of sending me here is to provoke you.

14

If you lose your cool, your men will act blindly and rashly.

Never mind, charge and talk later!

15

Similarly, if you kill me, our soldiers will be enraged.

16

The commander of the Wu army will use my death to rouse the fighting spirit of his men.

The Jing devils are inhuman. Let's crush them today!

17

If my death can result in the protection of my state, isn't it auspicious?

18

He's right. If we kill him, we'll be falling into their trap.

19

I'd have lost my life if I didn't keep my cool and say the right thing.

Juwei Juerong was released.

20

Biyang is small but well defended. It's just not worth the risk.

During the Spring and Autumn Era, a request by Jin generals Xun Yan and Shi Gai to attack Biyang was turned down by Commander Zhi.

25

Get the job done before you talk to me again!

Commander Zhi shouted in feigned anger:

26

At the beginning, I didn't agree to attack Biyang. But for the sake of military unity, I didn't oppose.

27

You convinced the marquis to drag me along and now you refuse to try hard to capture the city. You must be trying to put the blame on me.

If we go back now, you'll tell the marquis:

28

Commander Zhi ordered a retreat. Otherwise we'd have captured the city.

Tho old man really means business.

I'm old and weak. I won't be able to take another rap. You'll take the city in seven days or off with your heads!

Shaken by the commander's anger, Xun Yan and Shi Gai fought bravely, directing their troops in non-stop attacks on the city.

Stop attacking! We surrender. We'll pledge our allegiance to you from now on.

The Biyang defence collapsed after just a few days.

32

The Jin army marched into Biyang city.

33

If I didn't feign anger, you'd probably have lost confidence.

We really admire your resourcefulness, sir!

A commander should bear in mind the four elements of careful deliberation, bravery, timely action and justified anger. His timely action and justified anger will decide the combat strength of his troops.

34

1

A luring bait is bound to catch some fish.

Keep promises of reward and courtesy.

2

Reward

A handsome reward is bound to attract men to serve with a readiness to die.

3

During the Spring and Autumn Era, Viscount Jian of Zhao led his troops to intercept a Zheng army escorting army provisions. The two armies met at Qidi.

4 On the eve of battle, Viscount Jian announced:

This is going to be the battle in which we conform with Heaven's wishes and uphold justice.

5 Win this battle and every man will be rewarded. A senior official will be bestowed a county.

6 A junior official will be bestowed a prefecture.

7 An officer who has rendered meritorious service will be granted 100,000 *mu** of farmland.

8 Common people, workers and businessmen who have rendered meritorious service can become officials.

I never thought I could get a taste of becoming an official.

9 Slaves who have rendered meritorious service can become free people.

Long live freedom!

10 The viscount went on to talk about punishment for himself.

If we lose and I'm guilty, hang me!

* 1 mu = 0.07 hectare

14

As soon as the attack order was given, the
viscount's troops rushed forward to fight,
swiftly crushing the Zheng army
and capturing 1,000 cart loads
of army provisions.

15

What makes warriors fight selflessly is
reward and what makes able men pledge
their allegiance are courtesy and respect.

Courtesy

Treatment
with courtesy
and respect.

To understand the enemy situation is the essence of the art of warfare.

During the Warring States Era, Prince Xingling Jun of Wei was very particular about knowing everything about the enemy situation.

The more intelligence the better!

Once, the prince was having a game of chess with the king of Wei when a scout rushed in.

A Zhao army has set off towards our border!

Tyranny and onerous taxes presage a country's demise.

I'll do anything to be emperor!

Emperor Yang Guang of the Sui Dynastry was among the worst despots in Chinese history. He usurped the throne by murdering his father and elder brother.

For his enjoyment, he built an eastern capital at Luoyang. More than two million civilians were conscripted a month for this project.

Why do they catch so many people, uncle?

To build the eastern capital for the emperor.

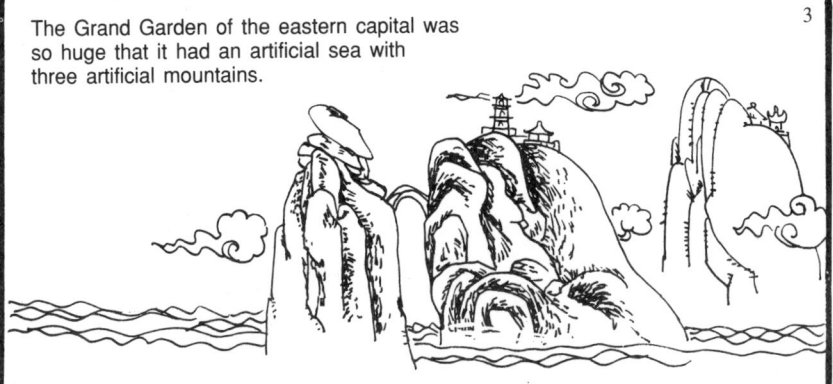

The Grand Garden of the eastern capital was so huge that it had an artificial sea with three artificial mountains.

4

Opulent pavilions and terraces were everywhere.

5

For its construction, huge logs were hauled over long distances by hundreds of thousands of forced labourers.

6

More than half of the men died of exhaustion and ill-treatment and were carried away by an endless stream of carts.

7

For the construction of the Great Wall,
1.2 million civilians were drafted.
Once, 600,000 men died within 10 days.

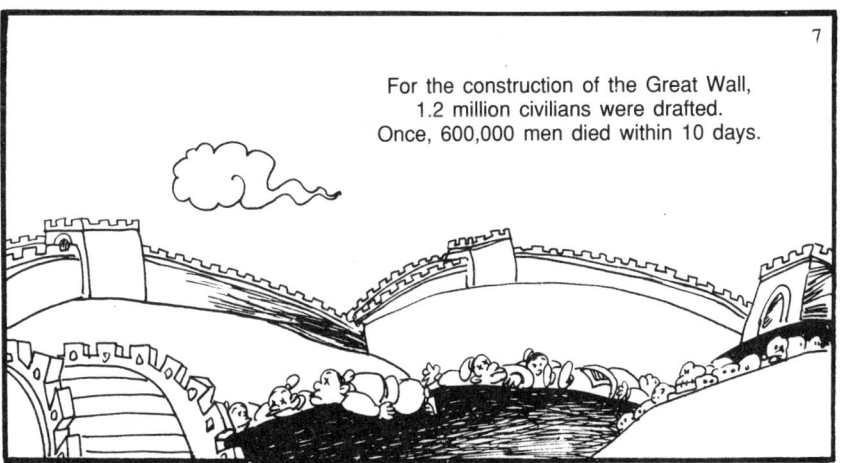

As able-bodied men became scarce,
even women were forced to do
corvee labour.

Thrice, the emperor went
on a cross-country river
tour. Each time, he was
escorted by thousands
of ships and hundreds
of thousands of soldiers.

9

10 Whenever his flotilla passed by a county, people within a radius of 250 km had to offer their best food.

11 Food that could not be finished was buried.

Delicious fish!

Superb meatballs!

12 Local officials who offered generous gifts were promoted and those who gave less were dismissed.

13 Going by the weight of this gift, you deserve a double promotion!

Round up everyone with the surname of Yang. Spare no one!

In the purge following a failed rebellion by Minister of Rites, Yang Xuangan, 30,000 people were executed and another 6,000 sent into exile.

14

15

You're eating your own child, brother!

I'm about to die of hunger!

Exorbitant taxes and tyrannical rule left the people with little to cling on to. In some areas hit by famine, there were even cases of cannibalism.

16

Forced by tyranny and onerous taxes, the people of Sui revolted. In the end, the despotic emperor was toppled and hanged by one of his generals.

83

The ruler who puts deceitful officials in important positions is in for disaster

1. In his later years, Emperor Xuanzong of the Tang Dynasty wanted to rest on what he had achieved and enjoy life.

Li Linfu's rather obedient. Making him the prime minister will save me a lot of trouble.

2. When consulted, Minister Zhang Jiuling said frankly:

The country will suffer if Li Linfu becomes prime minister!

3. The emperor disagreed.

He's all right. He won't bring disaster to the country.

4. While the emperor enjoyed life, Li arrogated all powers to himself.

His Majesty's busy. Talk to me if you've something to say!

Mt Hua has a gold mine. His Majesty still doesn't know...

Li Linfu set a trap for Premier Li Shizhi for whom he bore a grudge.

5

!?

Good news, Your Majesty! I've a way to make the country rich.

The unsuspecting premier rushed to see the emperor in joy.

6

7

Mt Hua has a gold mine. If we start mining...

8

Mt Hua's the sanctum of my divine life. Are you trying to kill me?

The emperor flew into a rage and snapped:

Framed by Li Linfu, Li Shizhi was relieved of his premiership and forced to take poison.

I never thought a loyal official would end up like this.

13

In a subsequent power struggle with Yang Guozhong, Li was defeated and killed. Yang became the premier.

I'm the brother-in-law of the emperor. I call the shots!

14

Submit and you'll prosper, resist and you'll perish!

Yang Guozhong, elder brother of the emperor's favourite concubine, Yang Guifei, arrogated 40 official posts to himself.

15

When deceitful ministers are in power, the entire army will be resentful.

Humph!

What has Yang Guozhong done to deserve the premiership!

16

These treacherous ministers always abuse their powers and act against the wishes of the people.

Stop arguing. Just do what I said!

17

18

Yes, I saw it personally the other day!

I heard that elephant's tasks may grow out of a dog's mouth.

They are unprincipled and are quick to please the ruler by echoing his views.

19

They are jealous of able men and will try to slander them.

They have no criteria on what is good and what is evil.

It's good if it pleases me. It's evil if it doesn't.

20

21

Duke Huan of Qi achieved hegemony during the Warring States Era with help from his able premier Guan Zhong.

I really appreciate all the help you've given me.

22

Before Guan Zhong died, he said to Duke Huan:

I hope you'll distance yourself from Yi Ya, Shu Diao, Qi Fang and Chang Zhiwu. They're crooks and will harm you.

23

Xi Peng's honest and firm. He's the right man to rely on.

Duke Huan did not heed Guan Zhong's advice. Three years later, the four men rebelled against him and starved him to death in prison.

A country must be careful not to let treacherous officials gain power as they will bring ruin. Emperor Xuanzong gave high posts to the evil Li Linfu and Yang Guozhong and resulted in the An-Shi Rebellion.

24

Scrutinize different opinions and discern people of different talents.

1 The ruler must keep his eyes and ears open in order to discern right and wrong.

2 Criticism Slander Rumour Praise

The ruler must remain sober in the face of praises, slanders, criticisms and other opinions.

3 If the ruler engages worthy officials and able generals, evil men will withdraw.

7

The Zhongshan ruler is fatuous and immoral. How can I serve him?

8

That's why I think Le Yang is a righteous man that can be entrusted with such an onerous mission.

9

Le Yang also made a military vow.

Court-martial me if I allow my personal feelings to ruin the mission.

Military Vow

I trust you since you're so resolute.

Le Yang was appointed commanding general.

10

11

Le Yang, your son will die if you dare advance any further!

As expected, Le Yang's son was bound and pushed to the front line when the Wei forces arrived in Zhongshan Kingdom.

12

Meanwhile, rumours were circulating in Wei.

The Zhongshan ruler has agreed to give Le Yang half of his country!

13

Le Yang's conspiring with the Zhongshan ruler to attack Wei!

14

A flood of memorials impeaching Le Yang swamped the imperial court.

15

Just put them away!

Unmoved by the rumours, Marquis Wen did not even read them.

16

These gifts are sent by the marquis in appreciation of everyone's services.

Instead, the marquis sent gifts and regards to Le Yang and his men.

17

Renovate according to this plan. Use the best imported materials.

He also ordered Le Yang's residence to be renovated.

18

Touched by the gestures,
Le Yang led an all-out attack
on Zhongshan.

19

The Zhongshan ruler again paraded Le Yang's son on the city wall.

20

Le Yang, if you don't stop attacking, I'll make you a soup of your son's flesh!

95

A generous reward for the first soldier to penetrate the enemy defence!

Unperturbed, Le Yang stepped up the attack on the city.

21

The Zhongshan ruler ordered Le Yang's son to be cooked.

Send this bowl of soup to Le Yang and let him have a taste of his son!

22

The Zhongshan envoy arrived with a threat.

Your son's been killed and cooked. His wife and children'll be used for making soup too if you continue with your attack!

23

24 Le Yang grabbed the bowl of soup and drank it on the spot.

25 Thank your king for the soup. The day we capture your city, we'll have a pot ready for your king too!

26 The Zhongshan envoy fled.

27 The Zhongshan ruler was stunned by the envoy's report.

28

Knowing the fall of the city was inevitable, the Zhongshan ruler hanged himself.

29

Le Yang returned triumphantly. Marquis Wen held a banquet to celebrate his victory.

While the guests were enjoying themselves, the marquis gave an order.

Take out the chests for General Le Yang and send them to his house.

Le Yang was very pleased when he saw the sealed chests upon his return.

Hmmm, there must be lots of treasures in there.

But he found only memorials impeaching him.

Conspiracy!

Rebellion!

Collusion!

The
Middle Strategy

中略

The secret of
controlling generals
and officials

Govern according to the time and situation.

The Three Kings of the ancient past had no language with which to govern their subjects, yet the world attained great peace. No one was conscious of whose merit it was.

Who deserves the greatest merit?

What's he talking about?

1

2

Times have changed. We can no longer use the old method of "governing without words". Do some thinking and come up with a legal code.

The Five Emperors used language and established restrictive measures to maintain social order.

Don't mention it.

You've contributed a lot to the state.

At that time, the ruler and ministers were modest and would not talk about merits and rewards. Neither were they particular about propriety.

3

Now everything must go by ethics and moral principles. There must also be strict observance of propriety between the king and officials.

The kings of Xia, Shang and Zhou governed by ethics and moral principles and the people were compliant and submissive.

4

My respects to you, dad.

The rite between father and son.

After you, brother.

The order between brothers and between husband and wife.

5

6

The feudal lords assembled regularly
at the imperial court and the duty
of kingship was not neglected.

The
people were
governed
by law.

You're
sentenced to
death under
Section 489
of the
Penal Code.

Hegemons of the Spring and Autumn
Era substituted moral principles
and rites with political trickery
and craftiness.

A
hegemon
ought to
be sinister
and
ruthless.

8

9

10

11

12

17

Duke Xiang was planning his moves.

We'll attack Zheng first and then revive the Shang Dynasty.

18

The world has long forsaken the Shang Dynasty. Any attempt to revive it will only bring calamities.

High officials Gongsun Gu and Zi Yu advised against it.

19

Attacking Zheng and reviving Shang are righteous moves. That's final!

20

Threatened by the advancing Song army, Zheng sought help from Chu. This gave Chu an excuse to attack Song.

21

The Song army set up a battleline on the northern bank of the Hong River against the Chu army.

22

Soon, the Chu army arrived and started to cross the river.

The best time to attack the Chu troops is when they're mid-stream.

A righteous army doesn't win by taking advantage of other's precarious position.

23

After crossing the river, the Chu army began its battle formation.

How can a righteous army do such an unrighteous thing?

We're sure to win if we attack before their battle formation is ready.

24

The righteous army shall win. Charge!

When the Chu army was ready, Duke Xiang ordered the Song army to attack without regard for relative strength.

The numerically superior Chu army outflanked the Song troops.

25

Without righteousness, they can't achieve hegemony even if they win!

The Song army was soundly defeated. Duke Xiang barely escaped.

26

Idiot! Blockhead!

What a fool!

The people of Song blamed Duke Xiang for the defeat.

27

Allow full play to each person's talents.

Employ the wise, the courageous, the greedy and the stupid in different ways.

The wise like to establish their achievements.

The courageous love to realize their aspirations.

4

Ha! Ha! I've made another tidy profit.

The greedy fervently pursue profits.

5

The stupid do not mind sacrificing themselves.

6

During the Spring and Autumn Era, Qi attacked Chu.

Chu army commander, Zi Fa, led his troops in defence.

Both sides fought three battles and the Chu army lost every time.

8

9

Zi Fa tried using different tactics.

10

But the Qi army could not be beaten off. Instead, they were becoming more aggressive.

11

Zi Fa was at his wits' end.

Surrender seems to be the only way out.

12

Just then, a burglar came to see Zi Fa.

I have a way of scaring off the Qi army.

13

I know how to steal and I'm willing to try my skill in the enemy camp. Maybe I can turn the tide.

Well, go ahead and good luck!

The burglar sneaked into the enemy camp.

Tonight, I've brought back the mosquito net of the Qi commander.

Zi Fa asked a soldier to return it to the Qi commander.

This is indeed my mosquito net.

!

18

The following night...

19

My commander's sending this back to you so that you can sleep well.

Zi Fa again had the pillow returned to the Qi commander.

20

Hee! Hee!

On the third night, the burglar stole the Qi commander's hairpin.

21

Again, the hairpin was sent back to its owner.

Please be more careful in future.

22

At this rate, my head's going to be stolen too!

23

Retreat at once!

24

An important duty of the commander is to employ the right people so that everyone will be given the opportunity to use his talents fully.

The Qi army retreated hastily. Chu was saved by the skill of a mere burglar.

Attract talents with benevolence and righteousness.

1

I guarantee you great wealth if you work for me.

Righteous officers cannot be employed with material wealth alone.

2

?!

You're neither benevolent nor righteous. You aren't fit to order me about with your filthy money!

3

The wise would not serve a fatuous and obtuse ruler.

Why am I having only these low-IQ guys here?

During the Warring States Era, the king of Qin offered a large track of Qin territory in exchange for the feoff of Anling.

I'm offering land 10 times the size of Anling in exchange.

4

Not even for land 100 times the size!

But Anling Jun, the feoff's ruler, rejected the offer.

5

Anling Jun sent Tang Qie to Qin to decline the offer.

6

The king of Qin was furious.

Qin has crushed Han and Wei easily!

7

15

Nothing more than flinging his hat and knocking his head on the ground.

16

That's only the anger of a foolish individual.

17

The assassination of Wang Liao by Zhuang Zhu was an earthshaking event.

18

So were the assassination of Prince Qing Ji by Yao Li,

23

Please, we can always talk things over.

24

Now I know why Qin could crush Han and Wei yet Anling Jun could continue to exist with such a tiny territory.

Wealth and power are not almighty. Righteous men are attracted more by spiritual inspiration. Anling Jun was inferior to the king of Qin in terms of wealth but was superior in terms of benevolence and righteousness. That was why he had the support of people like Tang Qie.

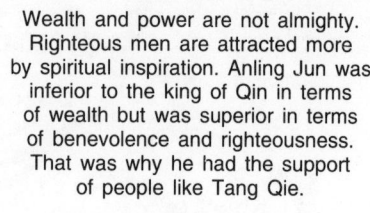

The king of Qin finally agreed not to pursue the land exchange matter.

25

One with morality and awesomeness is capable of great achievements.

If a ruler lacks morality, his ministers will rebel.

He's a veritable demon!

Do your words or ours matter?

If a ruler lacks awesomeness, he will not be able to control his country.

This rascal's immoral, so he can't be loyal to me.

A minister cannot be without morality.

7

Official Xian Renjia went into the palace to remonstrate with the king.

I've given an order: Those who dare to remonstrate with me will be put to death!

8

Aren't you afraid of death?

9

I only wish to let Your Majesty solve a riddle.

10

The king listened intently.

For three years, a huge bird on top of the southern mountain of Chu never flies nor sings.

Panel 11: Can you guess what bird that is, Your Majesty?

Panel 12: This is not an ordinary bird. It hasn't been making a move for three years because it's pondering on its future directions.

Panel 13: It hasn't been flying for three years because it's waiting for its wings to become more powerful. It hasn't been singing because it's observing the situation in Chu.

The king also promoted
five officials on the spot.

I know all of you are of high moral conduct and good calibre.

Letter of Appoint-ment

16

17

There is no place here for you!

He also sacked five incompetent officials.

18

Assisted by able officials, King Zhuang tightened internal administration and built up his military strength.

One who isn't adept at crafty manoeuvres can never win.

4

During the Spring and Autumn Era, Yang Chufu of Jin led an attack on Cai. A Chu army under Zi Shang came to the aid of Cai.

5

Hmmm, it doesn't pay to clash head-on with the Chus.

Yang Chufu decided to use tactical warfare.

6

If you want to fight, our army will retreat 30 *li** so that your army can cross the river and get ready your battle formation.

A Jin messenger was sent to Zi Shang.

133

* 1 li = 0.5 km

7

If you don't wish to cross the river and fight, please retreat 30 *li* so that our army can cross the river and get ready our battle formation.

8

The present stalemate is no good to either side. Please make your choice.

9

Zi Shang wanted to cross the river and fight but Da Sunbo advised against it.

We'll be in trouble if the Jins attack us when we're mid-stream.

10

The Chu army decided to retreat 30 *li*.

11

Ha! Ha! The Chu army has fallen into my trap!

Yang Chufu was very happy to see the Chu army retreat.

The Chus have been scared off. We've won!

Yang Chufu announced to the Jin soldiers:

12

The Jin army retreated unhurriedly home as if they had really won the war.

13

The Jin army has gone home.

That's strange. Why don't they cross the river to fight?

Zi Shang was surprised.

14

15 Without an opponent, Zi Shang led his troops home too.

The king of Chu was suspicious.

Why did he return without a fight?

16

17 Zi Shang must have been bribed by the Jins. This is a shame to Chu.

18 Have Zi Shang executed!

19 Until his death, Zi Shang never realized he had fallen into the trap of Yang Chufu.

Panel 20: During the Spring and Autumn Era, Guan Zhong of Qi was also a master strategist. One day, Duke Huan of Qi asked him:

I'm thinking of attacking Lu and Liang. Do you have any good scheme?

Panel 21: Lu and Liang customarily use *ti** for making clothes.

Panel 22: From now on, Your Majesty'll use *ti* for clothes and order all Qi people to follow suit.

* a silk and cotton fabric

137

23

Offenders will be beheaded!

Then Your Majesty'll ban the weaving of *ti* in Qi.

24

All the *ti* needed by Qi will have to be imported from Lu and Liang.

Qi

25

People in Lu and Liang will definitely give up farming in favour of *ti* weaving.

Wow, this is a money spinner!

26

I understand. We'll act according to your scheme.

27

Guan Zhong invited businessmen from Lu and Liang and gave them an attractive offer.

Qi will buy all the *ti* you can supply at a good price.

The ruler of Lu was very happy.

Let's mobilize the whole nation to weave *ti*.

28

29

The Liang ruler too, did not want to be left behind.

We must capture this huge market in Qi.

38

The two states could not even get conscripts for their armies.

39

Many of their starving soldiers also deserted and went to Qi.

40

Stratagems can change the relative strength of two armies without the use of force. The weak can take advantage of various conditions to beat a superior enemy, and the wise can beat their opponents without doing battles.

In less than three years, Lu and Liang surrendered to Qi.

Give meritorious officials good treatment.

When birds in the sky have all been shot, then the good bows should be stored away.

Now that the enemy states have all been crushed, meritorious ministers should be eliminated.

It doesn't mean killing them but just stripping them of their military powers.

These officials should also be handsomely rewarded for their good services.

5

This is what the court's given me!

This is what the court's given me!

They should also be enfeoffed and awarded jewellery and beautiful women to make them happy.

6

I'll keep them for future use.

How to treat meritorious generals and officials after winning a war is a matter that a ruler must handle carefully.

7

During the war between Chu and Han, Liu Bang, in his attempt to strengthen his influence, enfeoffed seven feudal lords. Of these, Han Xin was the most powerful.

8

After Liu Bang had defeated Xiang Yu and become emperor, he was afraid of the enfeoffed feudal lords ganging up against him.

9

Xiang Yu's general, Zhong Limei, has sought shelter with Han Xin.

Someone informed against Han Xin before Liu Bang.

10

Liu Bang hated Zhong Limei because he was once besieged by him.

15

What shall I do then?

If that's the case, an attack on Han Xin now will force him to rebel.

16

There's a beautiful Yunmeng resort in the south. Your Majesty can invite the *zhu hou** for a meeting there.

17

When Han Xin turns up, he can be captured with just a few guards.

Liu Bang adopted the scheme and captured Han Xin.

18

19

Now I can set my mind at ease.

For fear of adverse public opinion, Liu Bang did not kill Han Xin but merely demoted him.

147

* feudal lords

20

I should've known better and rebelled!

Han Xin was kept under house arrest in Changan.

21

Being with the emperor is as dangerous as being with a tiger!

Subsequently, Han Xin was killed for really plotting a rebellion with his close friend Chen Xi.

Historians say it was Liu Bang's mistakes in handling his meritorious officials after winning the war that led to discontent among the *zhu hou* and rebellions all over the country. In this respect, he was not as shrewd as the founding emperor of the Song Dynasty who relieved his key ministers of their military powers and gave them handsome rewards so that everyone was happy.

22

The Lower Strategy

下略

The strategy of governing
with the ways of the sage
and the worthy

Able men are the foundation of a state.

1 Worthy men helping in governing a state can make it strong, prosperous and peaceful.

2 If the worthy men depart, the state will become weak and fragmented.

3 During the Spring and Autumn Era, Qin sent an envoy to Chu.

I'm planning to invade Chu. Go there on the pretext of viewing treasures and assess the situation.

Panel 4:
Shall we show the Qin envoy our national treasures Heshi Jade and Suihou Pearl?

The king of Chu conferred with his ministers after getting news of it.

Panel 5:
The envoy's intention is to assess our internal situation so that they can draw up a plan to invade us. The crux of the matter isn't the treasures but whether we've worthy officials.

Zhao Xixu said:

Panel 6:
The king of Chu agreed with Zhao Xixu.

You'll handle the Qin envoy when he's here.

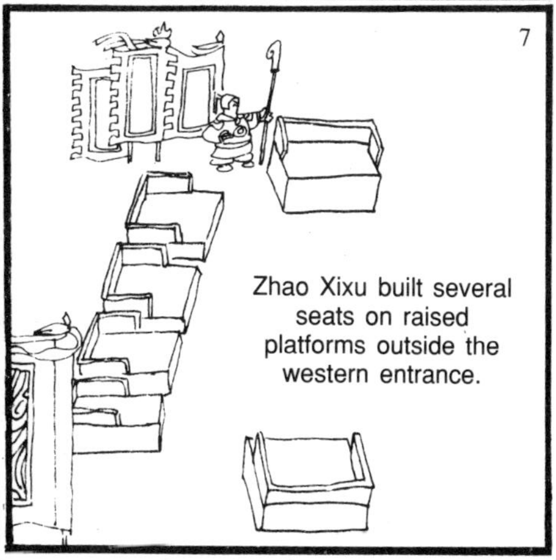

Panel 7:
Zhao Xixu built several seats on raised platforms outside the western entrance.

8

The Qin envoy was invited to be seated upon his arrival.

9

After the hosts and guest were seated, Zhao Xixu said:

Your Excellency wants to see our national treasures and here they are — our worthy ministers.

* Ling Yin, Tai Zong and other titles in italics were official designations in Chu

Panel 13:

Ye Gong* Zi Gao is in charge of border security. He doesn't invade neighbouring states but neither does he allow other states to invade us.

13

Panel 14:

14

Sima* Zi You is in charge of the army and military training.

154

15

16

155

The Qin envoy was speechless.

He left for home hastily to report his findings.

Whether it is a country or any organization, able men are always a guarantee of its success.

Chu can't be invaded. It has many worthy officials.

The king of Qin gave up the idea of invading Chu after being briefed by the envoy.

156

Win over the allegiance of men with exemplary conduct and sincerity.

3

During the Spring and Autumn Era, Jin attacked Chu. King Zhuang of Chu ordered:

Retreat 90 *li.*

4

But the Jin army still pursued closely.

5

May we launch a counter-attack to teach the Jins a lesson!

Ministers of Chu were furious and petitioned for battle.

6

During the time of the late king, Jin dared not invade Chu.

But they're doing it now when I'm on the throne.

7

8

This is all my fault. I haven't governed the state well. Our army isn't strong. How could I bear to let you risk your lives fighting the enemy?

9 The ministers were moved to tears.

10 The late king was assisted by other ministers and the Jins dared not invade us.

11 But they're doing it now when we're administering the state.

12 This is all our fault.

16

They're united. We can't possibly defeat them.

The Jin army retreated quietly in the night.

Don't let the Chu soldiers know!

17

Later, King Zhuang of Chu wanted to invade Jin.

Minister Tun Yin, will you go to Jin and make an assessment?

18

The Jin ruler is indulging in sensual pleasures.

He won't listen to any criticism or advice.

Don't be long-winded! I know what to do.

The Jin people hate their ruler.

If we attack Jin now, its people will definitely rise in revolt.

Attack Jin at once.

A virtuous ruler knows how to win over his people by setting an example with his own conduct and influencing them with sincerity and ethical education.

As Tun Yin had predicted, Jin fell without much resistance.

Put orders into effect to ensure success.

1

When orders are not put into effect, then government cannot be properly established and the state cannot be administered well.

I order you to lead an attack on the enemy state!

I'm not feeling well. I'll see what I can do when I get better.

2

During the Warring States Era, Wu Qi was once the garrison commander of Xihe Prefecture of Wei. He wanted to capture a Qin pavilion outpost on the border.

Qin soldiers often used the pavilion as a base for making incursions into Wei territory.

The Wei people could not farm in peace.

It's not worth a major recruitment exercise to get soldiers for capturing such a small pavilion.

6

Wu Qi had an idea. He put a cart shaft outside the northern gate and announced:

He who carries this to the outside of the southern gate will get a reward of fine farmland and a house.

7

At the beginning, no one cared to try.

This is too good to be true.

This must be a joke.

8

Eventually, someone took up the offer.

Hee!
Hee!
Ha!
Ha!

12

We'll be attacking the Qin pavilion tomorrow. He who gets in first will be promoted and rewarded handsomely.

Knowing the time was ripe, Wu Qi announced:

13

The following day, as soon as the order was given, soldiers and commoners scrambled to charge forward.

What proceeds from the ruler and descends to the minister is called "commands". What is recorded on bamboo strips and silk is called "orders". What is implemented is called "government". Only when orders are duly put into effect and the government is established will a state become successful.

Before the morning was over, Wei soldiers and commoners had captured the Qin pavilion.

14

Befriend worthies and shun villains.

If you dismiss or mistreat a worthy man, many worthy men will distance themselves from you.

So what if you're learned? Big deal!

Hmmm! You can kill a worthy man but not insult him!

Reward an evil man and many evil men will flock to you.

It seems Zhang Dalai's made it rich there. Let's try our luck too.

4

When the good are rewarded and the evil are punished, the state will be secure and prosperous.

Virtuous

Able

5

In the final years of the Qin Dynasty, Li Shiqi, a poor old scholar, lived in Gao Yang.

6

Liu Bang and his army passed by Gao Yang on their way to attack the Qin capital of Xianyang.

7

Li Shiqi managed to find and visit a fellow native friend who served as a military officer in Liu Bang's army.

8

I've observed many *zhu hou* who passed this way.

9

But none of them impressed me as someone with the potential of great achievements.

10

I heard that Liu Bang's a man of great talent and bold vision despite his arrogance.
He's the type of man I'd like to serve.
Would you please recommend me to him?

18

If you're serious about destroying Qin, why are you greeting an elder person sitting down?

19

You need strategists and worthy men to assist you in the war. Who would come forward to help you if you were so arrogant?

20

Thereupon, Liu Bang rose, straightened his clothes and said:

Please sit down, mister!

21

Li Shiqi went on to give an eloquent analysis of the achievements and failures of the six states.

Success　Failure　Rise　Fall

Liu Bang was elated.

Great! You'll go first, mister, and I'll follow with my men.

The superior strategy is, therefore, to occupy Chenliu, then recruit more men before advancing towards Guanzhong.

26

Millet

Rice

It's all your credit. I hereby grant you the title of Guangye Jun.

With the help of Li Shiqi, Liu Bang easily captured Chenliu and obtained large quantities of military provisions.

27

28

In the struggle for supremacy in the final years of the Qin Dynasty, Liu Bang often lost out to Xiang Yu because of his inferior strength. In the end, however, Liu Bang prevailed. This could be attributed to his skill in winning over able men and giving them important positions at ordinary times.

Because Liu Bang treated able men with courtesy and respect, he gained their support and eventually became the emperor.

178

Be far-sighted and plan well in advance.

The sage and the gentleman are able to perceive the sources of flourish and decline.

Flourish — Decline

The sage should understand the beginnings of success and defeat...

ascertain the crux of governing and turbulence, and knowing the measure of advancing and retreating.

4

During the Warring States Era, Qi attacked Song.

5

Song sent Zang Sun to seek help from Chu.

We'd appreciate your help.

6

Don't worry. I'll see to that personally.

7

Mission completed at last.

The king of Song will be very happy.

Those who came with Zang Sun were very happy.

180

12

A resolute Song defence will exhaust the Qi army. This will be to the advantage of Chu.

13

Hee! Hee! I've managed to pare the strength of Qi without the use of a single soldier.

14

That's why I say the king of Chu will never send reinforcement to the aid of Song.

183

Do not start a war casually.

A sage king does not take pleasure in waging a war but uses it to destroy a despot.

Wars are inauspicious instruments abhorred by Heaven's will.

However, when their employment is unavoidable in order to stop the violently perverse from harming the people, then waging a war accords with Heaven's will.

3

4

During the Warring States Era, Han and Zhao were engaged in a fierce battle.

Han sent an envoy to seek help from Wei.

May Your Majesty send a reinforcement to teach the Zhao devils a lesson.

5

6

The king of Zhao and I are like brothers. I'm sorry I can't oblige.

7

The king of Han was furious after being briefed by his envoy.

The king of Wei wouldn't even send a single soldier to our aid.

Several days later, Zhao also sent an envoy to Wei.

If Your Majesty will send troops to help us defeat the Hans...

We'll share with you all the land we get.

The king of Han and I are like brothers. How can I send troops to fight against him?

8

9

10

11

The king of Wei said he and the king of Han were like brothers and he couldn't send troops.

The king of Zhao was furious too.

12

Unable to borrow troops from Wei, Han and Zhao gave up fighting each other and withdrew their respective forces.

Later, when the truth emerged, the kings of Han and Zhao came to thank the king of Wei. As a result, the reputation of the king of Wei was greatly enhanced.

Wars happen regardless of whether men like them or not. Do not start an "unrighteous" war. If a war is unavoidable for the sake of eliminating tyranny or punishing the rebellious, casualties should be minimized.

The refusal was for the sake of peace. How noble!

188

13

Strategy & Leadership Series by Wang Xuanming

Thirty-six Stratagems: Secret Art of War
Translated by Koh Kok Kiang (cartoons) &
Liu Yi (text of the stratagems)
A Chinese military classic which emphasizes deceptive schemes to achieve military objectives. It has attracted the attention of military authorities and general readers alike.

Six Strategies for War: The Practice of Effective Leadership
Translated by Alan Chong
A powerful book for rulers, administrators and leaders, it covers critical areas in management and warfare including: how to recruit talents and manage the state; how to beat the enemy and build an empire; how to lead wisely; and how to manoeuvre brilliantly.

Gems of Chinese Wisdom: Mastering the Art of Leadership
Translated by Leong Weng Kam
Wise up with this delightful collection of tales and anecdotes on the wisdom of great men and women in Chinese history, including Confucius, Meng Changjun and Gou Jian.

Three Strategies of Huang Shi Gong: The Art of Government
Translated by Alan Chong
Reputedly one of man's oldest monograph on military strategy, it unmasks the secrets behind brilliant military manoeuvres, clever deployment and control of subordinates, and effective government.

100 Strategies of War: Brilliant Tactics in Action
Translated by Yeo Ai Hoon
The book captures the essence of extensive military knowledge and practice, and explores the use of psychology in warfare, the importance of building diplomatic relations with the enemy's neighbours, the use of espionage and reconnaissance, etc.

Asiapac Comic Series (by Tsai Chih Chung)

 **Art of War**
Translated by Leong Weng Kam
The Art of War provides a compact set of principles essential for victory in battles; applicable to military strategists, in business and human relationships.

 **Book of Zen**
Translated by Koh Kok Kiang
Zen makes the art of spontaneous living the prime concern of the human being. Tsai depicts Zen with unfettered versatility; his illustrations spans a period of more than 2,000 years.

 **Da Xue**
Translated by Mary Ng En Tzu
The second book in the Four Books of the Confucian Classics. It sets forth the higher principles of moral science and advocates that the cultivation of the person be the first thing attended to in the process of the pacification of kingdoms.

 **Fantasies of the Six Dynasties**
Translated by Jenny Lim
Tsai Chih Chung has creatively illustrated and annotated 19 bizarre tales of human encounters with supernatural beings which were compiled during the Six Dyansties (AD 220-589).

 **Lun Yu**
Translated by Mary Ng En Tzu
A collection of the discourses of Confucius, his disciples and others on various topics. Several bits of choice sayings have been illustrated for readers in this book.

 **New Account of World Tales**
Translated by Alan Chong
These 120 selected anecdotes tell the stories of emperors, princes, high officials, generals, courtiers, urbane monks and lettered gentry of a turbulent time. They afford a stark and amoral insight into human behaviour in its full spectrum of virtues and frailties and glimpses of brilliant Chinese witticisms, too.

Origins of Zen
Translated by Koh Kok Kiang

Tsai in this book traces the origins and development of Zen in China with a light-hearted touch which is very much in keeping with the Zen spirit of absolute freedom and unbounded creativity.

Records of the Historian
Translated by Tang Nguok Kiong

Adapted from Records of the Historian, one of the greatest historical work China has produced, Tsai has illustrated the life and characteristics of the Four Lords of the Warring Strates.

Roots of Wisdom
Translated by Koh Kok Kiang

One of the gems of Chinese literature, whose advocacy of a steadfast nature and a life of simplicity, goodness, quiet joy and harmony with one's fellow beings and the world at large has great relevance in an age of rapid changes.

Sayings of Confucius
Translated by Goh Beng Choo

This book features the life of Confucius, selected sayings from The Analects and some of his more prominent pupils. It captures the warm relationship between the sage and his disciples, and offers food for thought for the modern readers.

Sayings of Han Fei Zi
Translated by Alan Chong

Tsai Chih Chung retold and interpreted the basic ideas of legalism, a classical political philosophy that advocates a draconian legal code, embodying a system of liberal reward and heavy penalty as the basis of government, in his unique style.

Sayings of Lao Zi
Translated by Koh Kok Kiang & Wong Lit Khiong

The thoughts of Lao Zi, the founder of Taoism, are presented here in a light-hearted manner. It features the selected sayings from Dao De Jing.

Sayings of Lao Zi Book 2
Translated by Koh Kok Kiang
In the second book, Tsai Chih Chung has tackled some of the more abstruse passages from the Dao De Jing which he has not included in the first volume of Sayings of Lao Zi.

Sayings of Lie Zi
Translated by Koh Kok Kiang
A famous Taoist sage whose sayings deals with universal themes such as the joy of living, reconciliation with death, the limitations of human knowledge, the role of chance events.

Sayings of Mencius
Translated by Mary Ng En Tzu
This book contains stories about the life of Mencius and various excerpts from "Mencius", one of the Four Books of the Confucian Classics, which contains the philosophy of Mencius.

Sayings of Zhuang Zi
Translated by Goh Beng Choo
Zhuang Zi's non-conformist and often humorous views of life have been creatively illustrated and simply presented by Tsai Chih Chung in this book.

Sayings of Zhuang Zi Book 2
Translated by Koh Kok Kiang
Zhuang Zi's book is valued for both its philosophical insights and as a work of great literary merit. Tsai's second book on Zhuang Zi shows maturity in his unique style.

Strange Tales of Liaozhai
Translated by Tang Nguok Kiong
In this book, Tsai Chih Chung has creatively illustrated 12 stories from the Strange Tales of Liaozhai, an outstanding Chinese classic written by Pu Songling in the early Qing Dynasty.

Zhong Yong
Translated by Mary Ng En Tzu
Zhong Yong, written by Zi Si, the grandson of Confucius, gives voice to the heart of the discipline of Confucius. Tsai has presented it in a most readable manner for the modern readers to explore with great delight.

《亞太漫畫系列》

智謀叢畫

黃石公三略

編繪：王宣銘

翻譯：張家榮

亞太圖書有限公司出版